Mark Ford
Enter, Fleeing

Emily Berry
Stranger Baby

Durs [Grünbein]
Breakfast
Selected Poems
Translated by Michael Hofmann

Hannah [Sullivan]
[Three]
Poems

August Kleinzahler
The Hotel Oneira

Nick Laird
Go Giants

Lachlan Mackinnon
The Jupiter Collisions

Lachlan Mackinnon
Doves

Edwin Muir
Selected Poems

Bernard O'Donoghue
The Seasons of Cullen Church

W. H. Auden
Collected Longer Poems

Zaffar Kunial
Us

Stephen Spender
New Collected Poems

Wallace Stevens
Selected Poems

Jack Underwood
Happiness

Adam Zagajewski
Selected Poems

This diary belongs to

....

First published in 2021
by Faber & Faber Ltd
Bloomsbury House
74–77 Great Russell Street
London WC1B 3DA

Designed and typeset by Faber & Faber Ltd
Printed in Turkey

Clauses in the Banking and Financial Dealings Act allow
the government to alter dates at short notice

A CIP record for this book is available from the British Library

ISBN 978–0–571–36733–7

Faber & Faber

Poetry Diary

2022

... but its roots go back further to the Scientific Press, which started publishing in the early years of the century. The press's largest shareholders were Sir Maurice and Lady Gwyer, and their desire to expand into general publishing led them to Geoffrey Faber, a fellow of All Souls College, Oxford. Faber and Gwyer was founded in 1925. After four years Faber took the company forward alone, and the story goes that Walter de la Mare suggested adding a second, fictitious Faber to balance the company name.

In the meantime, the firm had prospered. T. S. Eliot, who had been suggested to Geoffrey Faber by a colleague at All Souls, had left Lloyds Bank in London to join him as a director, and in its first season the firm issued Eliot's *Poems 1909–1925*. In addition, the catalogues from the early years included books by Jean Cocteau, Herbert Read and Vita Sackville-West.

Poetry was always to be a significant element in the list and under Eliot's aegis Marianne Moore, Louis MacNeice and David Jones soon joined Ezra Pound, W. H. Auden, Stephen Spender, James Joyce, Siegfried Sassoon, D. H. Lawrence and Walter de la Mare.

Under Geoffrey Faber's chairmanship the board in 1929 included Eliot, Richard de la Mare, Charles Stewart and Frank Morley. This young team built up a comprehensive and profitable catalogue distinguished by modern design, much of which is still in print. Biographies, memoirs, fiction, poetry, political and religious essays, art and architecture monographs, children's books and a pioneering range of ecology titles contributed towards an eclectic list full of character. Faber also produced Eliot's groundbreaking literary review *The Criterion*.

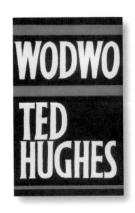

The Second World War brought both paper shortages and higher taxes, and the post-war years continued to be difficult. However, as the economy recovered a new generation of writers joined Faber, including William Golding, Robert Lowell, Ted Hughes, Sylvia Plath, Seamus Heaney, Philip Larkin, Thom Gunn and P. D. James. The publishing of Samuel Beckett and John Osborne began the firm's commitment to a modern drama list that now includes Tom Stoppard, Harold Pinter and David Hare.

From the 1970s through to the 1990s there was a blossoming in literary fiction, with the addition of authors such as Peter Carey, Kazuo Ishiguro, Barbara Kingsolver, Milan Kundera, Mario Vargas Llosa and Orhan Pamuk.

The year 2022 finds the publishing company that Geoffrey Faber founded remaining true to the principles he instigated and independent of corporate ownership. In over ninety years of publishing, Faber & Faber can count among its authors seven Carnegie Medal winners, three Kate Greenaway Medal winners, more than twenty Whitbread/Costa Book Award winners, seven Man Booker Prize winners, twelve Forward Poetry Prize winners, and thirteen Nobel Laureates.

In addition to dedicated core publishing, recent years have seen some new strands emerge, including a distinctive Faber Audio list, the launch of the Faber Academy writing school and a Faber Members programme.

A more detailed chronology of Faber & Faber's poetry publishing appears at the back of this diary.

JANUARY

M	T	W	T	F	S	S
27	28	29	30	31	1	2
3	4	5	6	7	8	9
10	11	12	13	14	15	16
17	18	19	20	21	22	23
24	25	26	27	28	29	30
31	1	2	3	4	5	6

FEBRUARY

M	T	W	T	F	S	S
31	1	2	3	4	5	6
7	8	9	10	11	12	13
14	15	16	17	18	19	20
21	22	23	24	25	26	27
28	1	2	3	4	5	6
7	8	9	10	11	12	13

MARCH

M	T	W	T	F	S	S
28	1	2	3	4	5	6
7	8	9	10	11	12	13
14	15	16	17	18	19	20
21	22	23	24	25	26	27
28	29	30	31	1	2	3
4	5	6	7	8	9	10

APRIL

M	T	W	T	F	S	S
28	29	30	31	1	2	3
4	5	6	7	8	9	10
11	12	13	14	15	16	17
18	19	20	21	22	23	24
25	26	27	28	29	30	1
2	3	4	5	6	7	8

MAY

M	T	W	T	F	S	S
25	26	27	28	29	30	1
2	3	4	5	6	7	8
9	10	11	12	13	14	15
16	17	18	19	20	21	22
23	24	25	26	27	28	29
30	31	1	2	3	4	5

JUNE

M	T	W	T	F	S	S
30	31	1	2	3	4	5
6	7	8	9	10	11	12
13	14	15	16	17	18	19
20	21	22	23	24	25	26
27	28	29	30	1	2	3
4	5	6	7	8	9	10

JULY

M	T	W	T	F	S	S
27	28	29	30	1	2	3
4	5	6	7	8	9	10
11	12	13	14	15	16	17
18	19	20	21	22	23	24
25	26	27	28	29	30	31
1	2	3	4	5	6	7

AUGUST

M	T	W	T	F	S	S
1	2	3	4	5	6	7
8	9	10	11	12	13	14
15	16	17	18	19	20	21
22	23	24	25	26	27	28
29	30	31	1	2	3	4
5	6	7	8	9	10	11

SEPTEMBER

M	T	W	T	F	S	S
29	30	31	1	2	3	4
5	6	7	8	9	10	11
12	13	14	15	16	17	18
19	20	21	22	23	24	25
26	27	28	29	30	1	2
3	4	5	6	7	8	9

OCTOBER

M	T	W	T	F	S	S
26	27	28	29	30	1	2
3	4	5	6	7	8	9
10	11	12	13	14	15	16
17	18	19	20	21	22	23
24	25	26	27	28	29	30
31	1	2	3	4	5	6

NOVEMBER

M	T	W	T	F	S	S
31	1	2	3	4	5	6
7	8	9	10	11	12	13
14	15	16	17	18	19	20
21	22	23	24	25	26	27
28	29	30	1	2	3	4
5	6	7	8	9	10	11

DECEMBER

M	T	W	T	F	S	S
28	29	30	1	2	3	4
5	6	7	8	9	10	11
12	13	14	15	16	17	18
19	20	21	22	23	24	25
26	27	28	29	30	31	1
2	3	4	5	6	7	8

JANUARY

M	T	W	T	F	S	S
28	29	30	31	1	2	3
4	5	6	7	8	9	10
11	12	13	14	15	16	17
18	19	20	21	22	23	24
25	26	27	28	29	30	31
1	2	3	4	5	6	7

FEBRUARY

M	T	W	T	F	S	S
1	2	3	4	5	6	7
8	9	10	11	12	13	14
15	16	17	18	19	20	21
22	23	24	25	26	27	28
1	2	3	4	5	6	7
8	9	10	11	12	13	14

MARCH

M	T	W	T	F	S	S
1	2	3	4	5	6	7
8	9	10	11	12	13	14
15	16	17	18	19	20	21
22	23	24	25	26	27	28
29	30	31	1	2	3	4
5	6	7	8	9	10	11

APRIL

M	T	W	T	F	S	S
29	30	31	1	2	3	4
5	6	7	8	9	10	11
12	13	14	15	16	17	18
19	20	21	22	23	24	25
26	27	28	29	30	1	2
3	4	5	6	7	8	9

MAY

M	T	W	T	F	S	S
26	27	28	29	30	1	2
3	4	5	6	7	8	9
10	11	12	13	14	15	16
17	18	19	20	21	22	23
24	25	26	27	28	29	30
31	1	2	3	4	5	6

JUNE

M	T	W	T	F	S	S
31	1	2	3	4	5	6
7	8	9	10	11	12	13
14	15	16	17	18	19	20
21	22	23	24	25	26	27
28	29	30	1	2	3	4
5	6	7	8	9	10	11

JULY

M	T	W	T	F	S	S
28	29	30	1	2	3	4
5	6	7	8	9	10	11
12	13	14	15	16	17	18
19	20	21	22	23	24	25
26	27	28	29	30	31	1
2	3	4	5	6	7	8

AUGUST

M	T	W	T	F	S	S
26	27	28	29	30	31	1
2	3	4	5	6	7	8
9	10	11	12	13	14	15
16	17	18	19	20	21	22
23	24	25	26	27	28	29
30	31	1	2	3	4	5

SEPTEMBER

M	T	W	T	F	S	S
30	31	1	2	3	4	5
6	7	8	9	10	11	12
13	14	15	16	17	18	19
20	21	22	23	24	25	26
27	28	29	30	1	2	3
4	5	6	7	8	9	10

OCTOBER

M	T	W	T	F	S	S
27	28	29	30	1	2	3
4	5	6	7	8	9	10
11	12	13	14	15	16	17
18	19	20	21	22	23	24
25	26	27	28	29	30	31
1	2	3	4	5	6	7

NOVEMBER

M	T	W	T	F	S	S
1	2	3	4	5	6	7
8	9	10	11	12	13	14
15	16	17	18	19	20	21
22	23	24	25	26	27	28
29	30	1	2	3	4	5
6	7	8	9	10	11	12

DECEMBER

M	T	W	T	F	S	S
29	30	1	2	3	4	5
6	7	8	9	10	11	12
13	14	15	16	17	18	19
20	21	22	23	24	25	26
27	28	29	30	31	1	2
3	4	5	6	7	8	9

JANUARY

M	T	W	T	F	S	S
26	27	28	29	30	31	1
2	3	4	5	6	7	8
9	10	11	12	13	14	15
16	17	18	19	20	21	22
23	24	25	26	27	28	29
30	31	1	2	3	4	5

FEBRUARY

M	T	W	T	F	S	S
30	31	1	2	3	4	5
6	7	8	9	10	11	12
13	14	15	16	17	18	19
20	21	22	23	24	25	26
27	28	1	2	3	4	5
6	7	8	9	10	11	12

MARCH

M	T	W	T	F	S	S
27	28	1	2	3	4	5
6	7	8	9	10	11	12
13	14	15	16	17	18	19
20	21	22	23	24	25	26
27	28	29	30	31	1	2
3	4	5	6	7	8	9

APRIL

M	T	W	T	F	S	S
27	28	29	30	31	1	2
3	4	5	6	7	8	9
10	11	12	13	14	15	16
17	18	19	20	21	22	23
24	25	26	27	28	29	30
1	2	3	4	5	6	7

MAY

M	T	W	T	F	S	S
1	2	3	4	5	6	7
8	9	10	11	12	13	14
15	16	17	18	19	20	21
22	23	24	25	26	27	28
29	30	31	1	2	3	4
5	6	7	8	9	10	11

JUNE

M	T	W	T	F	S	S
29	30	31	1	2	3	4
5	6	7	8	9	10	11
12	13	14	15	16	17	18
19	20	21	22	23	24	25
26	27	28	29	30	1	2
3	4	5	6	7	8	9

JULY

M	T	W	T	F	S	S
26	27	28	29	30	1	2
3	4	5	6	7	8	9
10	11	12	13	14	15	16
17	18	19	20	21	22	23
24	25	26	27	28	29	30
31	1	2	3	4	5	6

AUGUST

M	T	W	T	F	S	S
31	1	2	3	4	5	6
7	8	9	10	11	12	13
14	15	16	17	18	19	20
21	22	23	24	25	26	27
28	29	30	31	1	2	3
4	5	6	7	8	9	10

SEPTEMBER

M	T	W	T	F	S	S
28	29	30	31	1	2	3
4	5	6	7	8	9	10
11	12	13	14	15	16	17
18	19	20	21	22	23	24
25	26	27	28	29	30	1
2	3	4	5	6	7	8

OCTOBER

M	T	W	T	F	S	S
25	26	27	28	29	30	1
2	3	4	5	6	7	8
9	10	11	12	13	14	15
16	17	18	19	20	21	22
23	24	25	26	27	28	29
30	31	1	2	3	4	5

NOVEMBER

M	T	W	T	F	S	S
30	31	1	2	3	4	5
6	7	8	9	10	11	12
13	14	15	16	17	18	19
20	21	22	23	24	25	26
27	28	29	30	1	2	3
4	5	6	7	8	9	10

DECEMBER

M	T	W	T	F	S	S
27	28	29	30	1	2	3
4	5	6	7	8	9	10
11	12	13	14	15	16	17
18	19	20	21	22	23	24
25	26	27	28	29	30	31
1	2	3	4	5	6	7

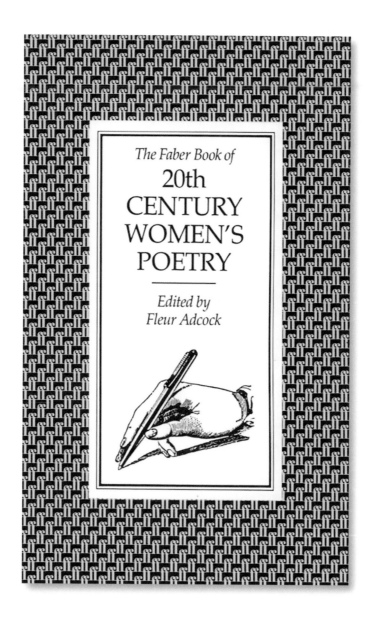

The Faber Book of
20th
CENTURY
WOMEN'S
POETRY

Edited by
Fleur Adcock

27 Monday CHRISTMAS DAY OBSERVED (UK, IRL, AUS, ZA, NZ, CAN)

28 Tuesday BOXING DAY HOLIDAY, ST STEPHEN'S DAY OBSERVED, DAY OF
GOODWILL OBSERVED (UK, IRL, AUS, ZA, NZ, CAN)

29 Wednesday

30 Thursday

31 Friday NEW YEAR'S EVE

1 Saturday NEW YEAR'S DAY   2 Sunday

Rainglobe

The warl' like an eemis stane
Wags i' the lift
— HUGH MACDIARMID

in this tilted
storm-knocked world —

this drop of Earth
that holds the lift —

how can we secure
the cobblestones to the coastal fog

or believe   that above the whirl
of cloud and flood

we might see — through whorls
on this stony sky —

the smudged wobble-handed
fingerprints of love

warl' — world;   eemis stane — unsteady stone;   lift — sky

Us (2018)

3 Monday NEW YEAR'S DAY OBSERVED (UK, IRL, AUS, ZA, NZ, CAN)
2ND JANUARY HOLIDAY (SCT)

4 Tuesday DAY AFTER NEW YEAR'S DAY (NZ)

5 Wednesday

6 Thursday

7 Friday

8 Saturday 9 Sunday

Winter Trees

The wet dawn inks are doing their blue dissolve.
On their blotter of fog the trees
Seem a botanical drawing —
Memories growing, ring on ring,
A series of weddings.

Knowing neither abortions nor bitchery,
Truer than women,
They seed so effortlessly!
Tasting the winds, that are footless,
Waist-deep in history —

Full of wings, otherworldliness.
In this, they are Ledas.
O mother of leaves and sweetness
Who are these pietàs?
The shadows of ringdoves chanting, but easing nothing.

Collected Poems (2002)

10 Monday

11 Tuesday

12 Wednesday

13 Thursday

14 Friday

15 Saturday   16 Sunday

Canopy

The weather was inside.

The branches trembled over the glass as if to apologise; then they thumped and they came in.

And the trees shook everything off until they were bare and clean. They held on to the ground with their long feet and leant into the gale and back again.

This was their way with the wind.

They flung us down and flailed above us with their visions and their pale tree light.

I think they were telling us to survive. That's what a leaf feels like anyway. We lay under their great awry display and they tattooed us with light.

They got inside us and made us speak; I said my first word in their language: 'canopy'.

I was crying and it felt like I was feeding. Be my mother, I said to the trees, in the language of trees, which can't be transcribed, and they shook their hair back, and they bent low with their many arms, and they looked into my eyes as only trees can look into the eyes of a person, they touched me with the rain on their fingers till I was all droplets, till I was a mist, and they said they would.

Stranger, Baby (2017)

17 Monday

18 Tuesday

19 Wednesday

20 Thursday

21 Friday

22 Saturday

23 Sunday

Daljit Nagra

British Museum

Poetry

ff

24 Monday

25 Tuesday BURNS NIGHT

26 Wednesday AUSTRALIA DAY (AUS)

27 Thursday

28 Friday

29 Saturday   30 Sunday

Alpha Step

A change to my usual sleeping position,
earth holding me close
like I'm something it loves.
I feel a murmur through the hedgerow,
old gods thawing from the permafrost.
Only a matter of time
before an empire falls
into the hands of an idiot,
and there are more ways of saying things
than things worth saying;
only a matter of steering the wind,
which batters us daily; this only life
that climbs beyond unfashionable
beginnings, leaving us leaving it,
breathless software, a bite taken out
of the grand old narrative,
while our ghosts refuel mid-air.
Deep time. Homely time.
The human print will not survive.
I mean like, woo, there it was.

A Year in the New Life (2021)

31 Monday

1 Tuesday

2 Wednesday

3 Thursday

4 Friday

5 Saturday   6 Sunday

A Wet Winter

from A Midsummer Night's Dream

Therefore the winds, piping to us in vain,
As in revenge have sucked up from the sea
Contagious fogs: which, falling in the land,
Hath every pelting river made so proud
That they have overborne their continents.
The ox hath therefore stretched his yoke in vain,
The ploughman lost his sweat, and the green corn
Hath rotted ere his youth attained a beard.
The fold stands empty in the drownèd field,
And crows are fatted with the murrion flock,
The nine men's morris is filled up with mud,
And the quaint mazes in the wanton green
For lack of tread are undistinguishable.

7 Monday WAITANGI DAY (NZ)

8 Tuesday

9 Wednesday

10 Thursday

11 Friday

12 Saturday

13 Sunday

The Fiddler of Dooney

When I play on my fiddle in Dooney,
Folk dance like a wave of the sea;
My cousin is priest in Kilvarnet,
My brother in Mocharabuiee.

I passed my brother and cousin:
They read in their books of prayer;
I read in my book of songs
I bought at the Sligo fair.

When we come at the end of time
To Peter sitting in state,
He will smile on the three old spirits,
But call me first through the gate;

For the good are always the merry,
Save by an evil chance,
And the merry love the fiddle,
And the merry love to dance:

And when the folk there spy me,
They will all come up to me,
With 'Here is the fiddler of Dooney!'
And dance like a wave of the sea.

POET TO POET *W. B. Yeats: Poems Selected by Seamus Heaney* (2000)

14 Monday · VALENTINE'S DAY

15 Tuesday

16 Wednesday

17 Thursday

18 Friday

19 Saturday   20 Sunday

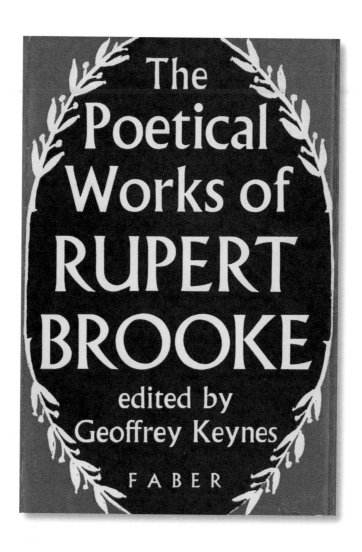

The
Poetical
Works of
RUPERT
BROOKE

edited by
Geoffrey Keynes

FABER

21 Monday

22 Tuesday

23 Wednesday

24 Thursday

25 Friday

26 Saturday

27 Sunday

It Rains

It rains, and nothing stirs within the fence
Anywhere through the orchard's untrodden, dense
Forest of parsley. The great diamonds
Of rain on the grassblades there is none to break,
Or the fallen petals further down to shake.

And I am nearly as happy as possible
To search the wilderness in vain though well,
To think of two walking, kissing there,
Drenched, yet forgetting the kisses of the rain:
Sad, too, to think that never, never again,

Unless alone, so happy shall I walk
In the rain. When I turn away, on its fine stalk
Twilight has fined to naught, the parsley flower
Figures, suspended still and ghostly white,
The past hovering as it revisits the light.

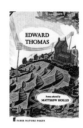

Selected Poems (2011)

28 Monday

1 Tuesday   ST DAVID'S DAY

2 Wednesday

3 Thursday

4 Friday

5 Saturday   6 Sunday

Every

Every ditch or stream or river the train crosses.
Every ploughed field, every row of trees.
Every square church tower in the distance.
Every minute of sunshine, every shadow.
Every wisp of cloud in the wide, blue, East Anglian sky.
Every day. Every day that's left.

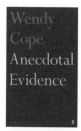

Anecdotal Evidence (2018)

7 Monday

8 Tuesday

9 Wednesday

10 Thursday

11 Friday

12 Saturday

13 Sunday

Spiegel im Spiegel

I swept away the heaps of broken glass
But I don't know where they went after that.
A repurposed, resurfaced Heaven perhaps

With its extra syllable for good luck
Like the way Spanish adds a rogue breath tucked
In front of the *s* in English words, 'start'

Becoming then 'estart' and 'Spider-man'
'Espider-man' as though the sad human
Sound that the snake makes could be saved from sin

By a little, inhaled inspiration,
Not a tech title – epoem, eRowan –
But rather a reminder of why sun

After sun after sun after sun comes
Back to us slightly more cracked at the core;
Because experience is translation

Of an event we were all a part of:
When the young, lonely god took the gloves off,
Shattered the black mirror, and called it love.

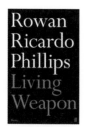

Living Weapon (2021)

14 Monday

15 Tuesday

16 Wednesday

17 Thursday ST PATRICK'S DAY (NI, IRL)

18 Friday

19 Saturday 20 Sunday

Collected
Poems

1925-1948

Louis
MacNeice

21 Monday   HUMAN RIGHTS DAY (ZA)

22 Tuesday

23 Wednesday

24 Thursday

25 Friday

26 Saturday   27 Sunday

April

from Prologue to The Canterbury Tales

Whan that Aprille with his shoures sote
The droghte of Marche hath perced to the rote,
And bathed every veyne in swich licour,
Of which vertu engendred is the flour;
Whan Zephirus eek with his swete breeth
Inspired hath in every holt and heeth
The tendre croppes, and the yonge sonne
Hath in the Ram his halfe cours y-ronne,
And smale fowles maken melodye,
That slepen al the night with open yë,
(So priketh hem nature in hir corages):
Than longen folk to goon on pilgrimages.

28 Monday

29 Tuesday

30 Wednesday

31 Thursday

1 Friday

2 Saturday

3 Sunday

The Donkey

When fishes flew and forests walked
    And figs grew upon thorn,
Some moment when the moon was blood
    Then surely I was born.

With monstrous head and sickening cry
    And ears like errant wings,
The devil's walking parody
    On all four-footed things.

The tattered outlaw of the earth,
    Of ancient crooked will;
Starve, scourge, deride me: I am dumb,
    I keep my secret still.

Fools! For I also had my hour;
    One far fierce hour and sweet:
There was a shout about my ears,
    And palms before my feet.

POETRY PLEASE (2013)

4   Monday

5   Tuesday

6   Wednesday

7   Thursday

8   Friday

9   Saturday   10   Sunday

Green

The dawn was apple-green,
   The sky was green wine held up in the sun,
The moon was a golden petal between.

She opened her eyes, and green
   They shone, clear like flowers undone
For the first time, now for the first time seen.

Winning Words: Inspiring Poems for Everyday Life (2012)

11 Monday

---

12 Tuesday

---

13 Wednesday

---

14 Thursday

---

15 Friday   GOOD FRIDAY (UK, AUS, ZA, NZ, CAN)

---

16 Saturday   EASTER (HOLY) SATURDAY   17 Sunday   EASTER SUNDAY

Michael
Hofmann
One Lark,
One Horse

Poetry

ff

18 Monday   EASTER MONDAY (UK, IRL, AUS, NZ)
            FAMILY DAY (ZA)

19 Tuesday

20 Wednesday

21 Thursday

22 Friday

23 Saturday   ST GEORGE'S DAY   24 Sunday

Spring

Nothing is so beautiful as spring –
   When weeds, in wheels, shoot long and lovely and lush;
   Thrush's eggs look little low heavens, and thrush
Through the echoing timber does so rinse and wring
The ear, it strikes like lightnings to hear him sing;
   The glassy peartree leaves and blooms, they brush
   The descending blue; that blue is all in a rush
With richness; the racing lambs too have fair their fling.

What is all this juice and all this joy?
   A strain of the earth's sweet being in the beginning
In Eden garden. – Have, get, before it cloy,
   Before it cloud, Christ, lord, and sour with sinning,
Innocent mind and Mayday in girl and boy,
   Most, O maid's child, thy choice and worthy the winning.

POET TO POET *Gerard Manley Hopkins: Poems Selected by John Stammers* (2012)

25 **Monday**   ANZAC DAY (AUS, NZ)

26 Tuesday

27 **Wednesday**   FREEDOM DAY (ZA)

28 Thursday

29 Friday

30 Saturday   1 Sunday

À Quoi Bon Dire

Seventeen years ago you said
    Something that sounded like Good-bye;
    And everybody thinks that you are dead,
        But I.

    So I, as I grow stiff and cold
To this and that say Good-bye too;
    And everybody sees that I am old
        But you.

    And one fine morning in a sunny lane
Some boy and girl will meet and kiss and swear
    That nobody can love their way again
        While over there
You will have smiled, I shall have tossed your hair.

Selected Poetry and Prose (2019)

2 **Monday** WORKERS' DAY (ZA)
EARLY MAY BANK HOLIDAY (UK)
MAY DAY (IRL)

3 Tuesday

4 Wednesday

5 Thursday

6 Friday

7 Saturday   8 Sunday

Last

God for a fortnight, pharaoh
till the generator blows, then what?
This week's most missed:
the shipping forecast; showing off.
Write ALIVE in the meadow
with empty blue oil drums in case
clouds can read/stars give a toss.
Two million years of shame
takes some shucking off – I still
nip behind a wall to exude.

Mandrake prospers in the cracks.
Corned beef and cling peaches again;
note to self: start growing stuff.
Along the station's oxidised tracks
every minute pulls in on time.
Ripples on the lake: ditto, ditto.
On the plus side my golf swing's
unrecognisable these days. Love is:
an afternoon in the glyptotheque
with Madam Kalashnikov.

Simon
Armitage
Sandettie
Light Vessel
Automatic

Sandettie Light Vessel Automatic (2019)

9 Monday

10 Tuesday

11 Wednesday

12 Thursday

13 Friday

14 Saturday 15 Sunday

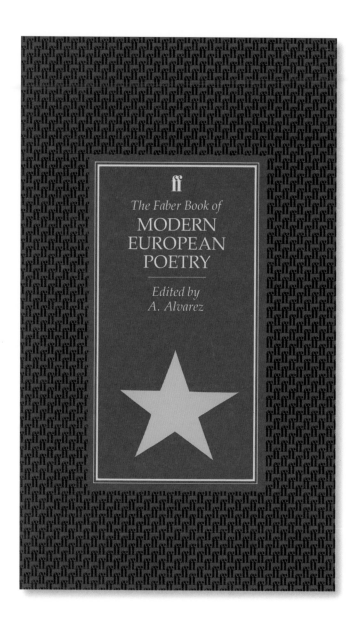

ff

The Faber Book of
MODERN
EUROPEAN
POETRY

Edited by
A. Alvarez

16 Monday

17 Tuesday

18 Wednesday

19 Thursday

20 Friday

21 Saturday

22 Sunday

The Iron Age Boat at Caumatruish

If you doubt, you can put your fingers
In the holes where the oar-pegs went.
If you doubt still, look past its deep mooring
To the mountains that enfold the corrie's
Waterfall of lace through which, they say,
You can see out but not in.
If you doubt that, hear the falcon
Crying down from Gneeves Bog
Cut from the mountain-top. And if you doubt
After all these witnesses, no boat
Dredged back from the dead
Could make you believe.

Selected Poems (2008)

23 Monday

24 Tuesday

25 Wednesday

26 Thursday

27 Friday

28 Saturday

29 Sunday

Wild Nights! Wild Nights!

Wild nights! Wild nights!
Were I with thee,
Wild nights should be
Our luxury!

Futile the winds
To a heart in port, –
Done with the compass,
Done with the chart.

Rowing in Eden!
Ah! the sea!
Might I but moor
To-night in thee!

30　Monday

31　Tuesday

1　Wednesday

2　Thursday　SPRING BANK HOLIDAY (UK)

3　Friday　PLATINUM JUBILEE BANK HOLIDAY (UK)

4　Saturday　　　　　　　　　5　Sunday

Eternity

He who binds to himself a joy
Does the wingèd life destroy;
But he who kisses the joy as it flies
Lives in eternity's sun rise.

POET TO POET *William Blake: Poems Selected by James Fenton* (2010)

6   Monday   JUNE BANK HOLIDAY (IRL)
             QUEEN'S BIRTHDAY HOLIDAY (NZ)

7   Tuesday

8   Wednesday

9   Thursday

10 Friday

11 Saturday   12 Sunday

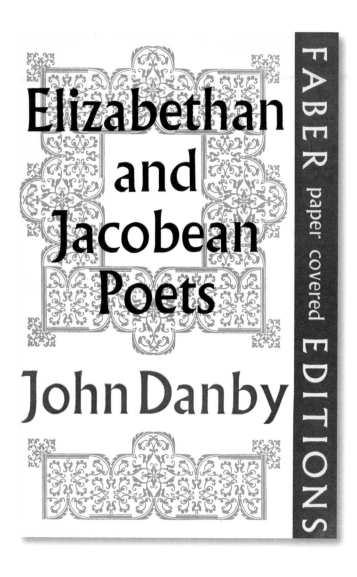

Elizabethan
and
Jacobean
Poets

John Danby

FABER paper covered EDITIONS

13 Monday

14 Tuesday

15 Wednesday

16 Thursday   YOUTH DAY (ZA)

17 Friday

18 Saturday   19 Sunday

Solar

Suspended lion face
Spilling at the centre
Of an unfurnished sky
How still you stand,
And how unaided
Single stalkless flower
You pour unrecompensed.

The eye sees you
Simplified by distance
Into an origin,
Your petalled head of flames
Continuously exploding.
Heat is the echo of your
Gold.

Coined there among
Lonely horizontals
You exist openly.
Our needs hourly
Climb and return like angels.
Unclosing like a hand,
You give for ever.

The Complete Poems (2012)

20 Monday

21 Tuesday

22 Wednesday

23 Thursday

24 Friday

25 Saturday

26 Sunday

A Glass of Wine

Exactly as the setting sun
clips the heel of the garden,

exactly as a pigeon
roosting tries to sing
and ends up moaning,

exactly as the ping
of someone's automatic carlock
dies into a flock
of tiny echo aftershocks,

a shapely hand of cloud
emerges from the crowd
of airy nothings that the wind allowed
to tumble over us all day
and points the way

towards its own decay,
but not before
a final sunlight-shudder pours
away across our garden floor

so steadily, so slow,
it shows you everything you need to know
about this glass I'm holding out to you,

its white, unblinking eye
enough to bear the whole weight of the sky.

27 Monday

28 Tuesday

29 Wednesday

30 Thursday

1 **Friday**   CANADA DAY (CAN)

2 Saturday   3 Sunday

Sonnet

The flag-top quivers in the breeze
That sighs among the willow trees;
In gentle waves the river heaves
That sways like boats the lily-leaves.
The bent-grass trembles as with cold
And crow-flowers nod their cups of gold
Till every dew-drop in them found
Is gently shook upon the ground.
Each wild weed by the river side
In different motions dignified
Bows to the wind, quakes to the breeze,
And charms sweet summer's harmonies.
The very nettle quakes away
To glad the summer's happy day.

POET TO POET *John Clare: Poems Selected by Paul Farley* (2007)

4 Monday

5 Tuesday

6 Wednesday

7 Thursday

8 Friday

9 Saturday

10 Sunday

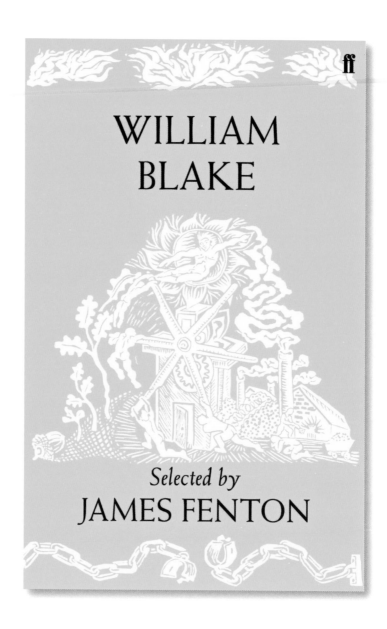

WILLIAM
BLAKE

Selected by
JAMES FENTON

11 Monday

12 Tuesday   BATTLE OF THE BOYNE (NI)

13 Wednesday

14 Thursday

15 Friday

16 Saturday   17 Sunday

Childhood among the Ferns

I sat one sprinkling day upon the lea,
Where tall-stemmed ferns spread out luxuriantly,
And nothing but those tall ferns sheltered me.

The rain gained strength, and damped each lopping frond,
Ran down their stalks beside me and beyond,
And shaped slow-creeping rivulets as I conned,

With pride, my spray-roofed house. And though anon
Some drops pierced its green rafters, I sat on,
Making pretence I was not rained upon.

The sun then burst, and brought forth a sweet breath
From the limp ferns as they dried underneath:
I said: 'I could live on here thus till death',

And queried in the green rays as I sate:
'Why should I have to grow to man's estate,
And this afar-noised World perambulate?'

POET TO POET *Thomas Hardy: Poems Selected by Tom Paulin* (2016)

18 Monday

19 Tuesday

20 Wednesday

21 Thursday

22 Friday

23 Saturday
24 Sunday

31

I promise when you cut your hair
and the curls fall
to mingle with the filthy leaves
the stares of boys and girls will arrive
like knives at your white neck
newly revealed
as if routed to their source
and with each long look
they'll style your lines again
becoming angular
as again the curls fall
your last weeks as a teenager
but slower this time
slowly like your early twenties

After Fame (2020)

25 Monday

26 Tuesday

27 Wednesday

28 Thursday

29 Friday

30 Saturday 31 Sunday

CHRISTINA ROSSETTI

Sleeping at Last

Sleeping at last, the trouble and tumult over,
    Sleeping at last, the struggle and horror past,
Cold and white, out of sight of friend and of lover,
      Sleeping at last.

    No more a tired heart downcast or overcast,
No more pangs that wring or shifting fears that hover,
    Sleeping at last in a dreamless sleep locked fast.

Fast asleep. Singing birds in their leafy cover
    Cannot wake her, nor shake her the gusty blast.
Under the purple thyme and the purple clover
      Sleeping at last.

Short and Sweet (2002)

1 **Monday**   AUGUST BANK HOLIDAY (SCT, IRL)

2 Tuesday

3 Wednesday

4 Thursday

5 Friday

6 Saturday   7 Sunday

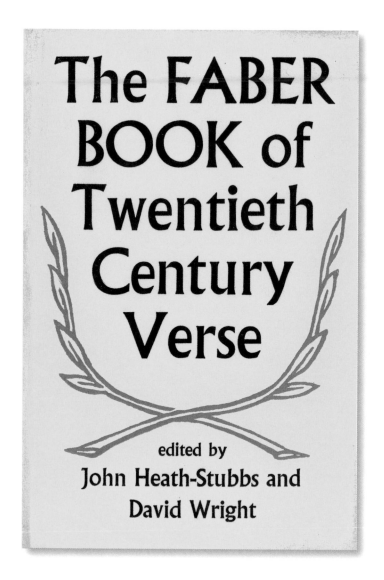

The FABER BOOK of Twentieth Century Verse

edited by
John Heath-Stubbs and
David Wright

8   Monday

9   Tuesday   NATIONAL WOMEN'S DAY (ZA)

10   Wednesday

11   Thursday

12   Friday

13   Saturday

14   Sunday

WCW

Saxifrage, said William Carlos Williams, was his flower
because it split stone. Yesterday, in a pot, a clump of it,
weedy red petals, stems robust as peasant legs.

It would survive a summer's rage for decking,
frost memory, meltwater gush, black August.
It wouldn't last a weekend in the jungle,

being a flower of the far north, temperate at best.
Williams was a doctor, and he could listen to his language
for the slightest sign, like a stethoscope.

Saxum is stone, frag the root of frangere, to break.
Latin names for northern things. Ghosts of empire.
Williams had time for the patient ones, men, women, children

who hang on, who pull through, saxifrage splitting stone.

Doves (2019)

15 Monday

16 Tuesday

17 Wednesday

18 Thursday

19 Friday

20 Saturday

21 Sunday

what my mother (a poet) might say (II)

be a river she might say
　　be the water that flows
　　　　over & under & along

so you will never hurt from
　　sharp things be the eyes
　　　　that glow be the body

whose scent & sound attract
　　all the colours of the night
　　　　be the rainbow that leaps

into that cleansed dome
　　of sky after storms erupt
　　　　from the breasts of millions

be the tree that praises
　　even when the cacophony
　　　　of tractors drown out its hymns

be the roots that seep
　　through stone be the echo
　　　　of your blood song of your bones

Flèche (2019)

22 Monday

23 Tuesday

24 Wednesday

25 Thursday

26 Friday

27 Saturday

28 Sunday

'The enemy of life'

The enemy of life, decayer of all kind,
That with his cold withers away the green,
This other night me in my bed did find,
And offered me to rid my fever clean;
And I did grant, so did despair me blind.
He drew his bow with arrow sharp and keen,
And struck the place where love had hit before,
And drove the first dart deeper more and more.

Short and Sweet (2002)

29 **Monday**   SUMMER BANK HOLIDAY (UK)

30 Tuesday

31 Wednesday

1 Thursday

2 Friday

3 Saturday   4 Sunday

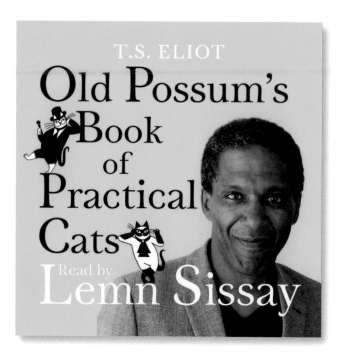

5 **Monday**   LABOUR DAY (CAN)

6 Tuesday

7 Wednesday

8 Thursday

9 Friday

10 Saturday   11 Sunday

Creature

Reading one September day
I felt it tickle the page
as if one of the letters
had broken free of the words.

It held two claws out in front,
the way a blindfolded man
protects himself from the wall.

I do not know what it was,
but I have set it down here

in case you should meet with one.

Wing (2020)

12 Monday

13 Tuesday

14 Wednesday

15 Thursday

16 Friday

17 Saturday

18 Sunday

Star

If, in the light of things, you fade
real, yet wanly withdrawn
to our determined and appropriate
distance, like the moon left on
all night among the leaves, may
you invisibly delight this house,
O star, doubly compassionate, who came
too soon for twilight, too late
for dawn, may your faint flame
strive with the worst in us
through chaos
with the passion of
plain day.

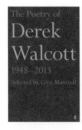

The Poetry of Derek Walcott 1948–2013 (2019)

19 Monday

20 Tuesday

21 Wednesday

22 Thursday

23 Friday

24 Saturday   HERITAGE DAY (ZA)   25 Sunday

Witchcraft by a picture

I fixe mine eye on thine, and there
    Pitty my picture burning in thine eye,
My picture drown'd in a transparent teare,
    When I looke lower I espie;
       Hadst thou the wicked skill
By pictures made and mard, to kill,
How many wayes mightst thou performe thy will?

But now I have drunke thy sweet salt teares,
    And though thou poure more I'll depart;
My picture vanish'd, vanish feares;
    That I can be endamag'd by that art;
      Though thou retaine of mee
One picture more, yet that will bee,
Being in thine owne heart, from all malice free.

POET TO POET *John Donne: Poems Selected by Paul Muldoon* (2012)

26 Monday

27 Tuesday

28 Wednesday

29 Thursday

30 Friday

1 Saturday

2 Sunday

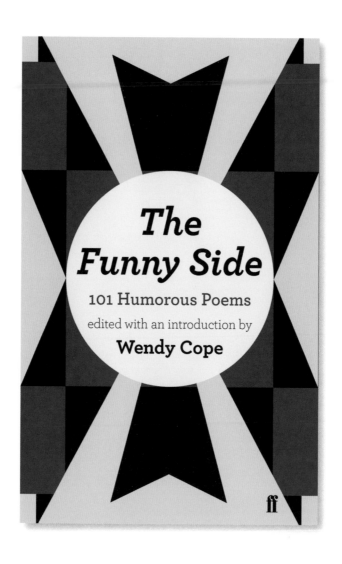

The
Funny Side

101 Humorous Poems

edited with an introduction by

Wendy Cope

ff

3 Monday

4 Tuesday

5 Wednesday

6 Thursday

7 Friday

8 Saturday   9 Sunday

With Ships the sea was sprinkled far and nigh

With Ships the sea was sprinkled far and nigh,
Like stars in heaven, and joyously it showed;
Some lying fast at anchor in the road,
Some veering up and down, one knew not why.
A goodly Vessel did I then espy
Come like a giant from a haven broad;
And lustily along the bay she strode,
Her tackling rich, and of apparel high.
This Ship was naught to me, nor I to her,
Yet I pursued her with a Lover's look;
This Ship to all the rest did I prefer:
When will she turn, and whither? She will brook
No tarrying; where She comes the winds must stir:
On went She, and due north her journey took.

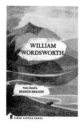

POET TO POET *William Wordsworth: Poems Selected by Seamus Heaney* (2005)

10 **Monday**   THANKSGIVING DAY (CAN)

11 Tuesday

12 Wednesday

13 Thursday

14 Friday

15 Saturday   16 Sunday

· Preludes

I

The winter evening settles down
With smell of steaks in passageways.
Six o'clock.
The burnt-out ends of smoky days.
And now a gusty shower wraps
The grimy scraps
Of withered leaves about your feet
And newspapers from vacant lots;
The showers beat
On broken blinds and chimney-pots,
And at the corner of the street
A lonely cab-horse steams and stamps.

And then the lighting of the lamps.

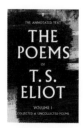

17 Monday

18 Tuesday

19 Wednesday

20 Thursday

21 Friday

22 Saturday

23 Sunday

The Changeling

After they found me hiding in the fork of the yew
I climbed into the chimney of the derelict house.
Curled in the bend, I saw the blue hole of the sky.
I liked silos, undersides of bridges, fields of tall maize.
I clambered onto bales to smoke under the barn roof.
Later, I lay down in a high-sided trailer and went to sleep.
When I woke I was out on the sand dunes under stars.

At school I lurked in the ball alley after lights-out,
or in the chapel by the glow from the tabernacle.
I thought you can hide in galleries and foreign cities,
in bars in daytime, even in a swimming pool.
There are hours you can spend loosely tethered to a lover.
There's the solace of watching over a sleeping baby.
The peace at night in the company of a dead body.

The Shoulder Tap (2021)

24 **Monday** LABOUR DAY (NZ)

25 Tuesday

26 Wednesday

27 Thursday

28 Friday

29 Saturday   30 Sunday

Ilya
Kaminsky
Deaf
Republic

Poetry

ff

3 1 Monday HALLOWEEN
OCTOBER BANK HOLIDAY (IRL)

1 Tuesday

2 Wednesday

3 Thursday

4 Friday

5 Saturday   6 Sunday

Remembrance Day

from Out

The poppy is a wound, the poppy is the mouth
Of the grave, maybe of the womb searching –

A canvas-beauty puppet on a wire
Today whoring everywhere. It is years since I wore one.

It is more years
The shrapnel that shattered my father's paybook

Gripped me, and all his dead
Gripped him to a time

He no more than they could outgrow, but, cast into one, like iron,
Hung deeper than refreshing of ploughs

In the woe-dark under my mother's eye –
One anchor

Holding my juvenile neck bowed to the dunkings of the Atlantic.

So goodbye to that bloody-minded flower.

You dead bury your dead.
Goodbye to the cenotaphs on my mother's breasts.

Goodbye to all the remaindered charms of my father's survival.

Let England close. Let the green sea-anemone close.

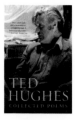

Collected Poems (2005)

7 Monday

8 Tuesday

9 Wednesday

10 Thursday

11 Friday REMEMBRANCE DAY (CAN)

12 Saturday   13 Sunday REMEMBRANCE SUNDAY

I May, I Might, I Must

If you will tell me why the fen
appears impassable, I then
will tell you why I think that I
can get across it if I try.

New Collected Poems (2017)

14 Monday

15 Tuesday

16 Wednesday

17 Thursday

18 Friday

19 Saturday

20 Sunday

Inkling

Last night I sensed a taking root
under the bonecage of my heart,
a stirring, shifting; something not
quite of a breath or heartbeat's weight.

It was the inkling of a soul.
Now I shall have no peace at all
till he's caught and fastened, nested in
the cradle of my pelvic bone.

Then, in the coracle of my womb,
I'll carry him gently, every inch home
though the hour is late
in the lengthening light

to the crook of my arm, the bay's curved shore,
water-lapped, twilit, secure.

Julia Copus
The
World's
Two
Smallest
Humans

The World's Two Smallest Humans (2012)

21 Monday

___

22 Tuesday

___

23 Wednesday

___

24 Thursday

___

25 Friday

___

26 Saturday   27 Sunday

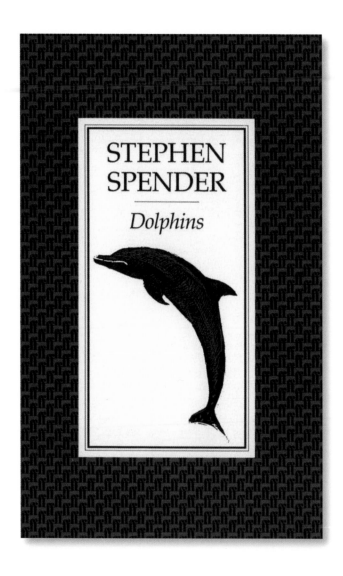

STEPHEN
SPENDER

Dolphins

28   Monday

29   Tuesday

30   Wednesday   ST ANDREW'S DAY HOLIDAY (SCT)

1   Thursday

2   Friday

3   Saturday   4   Sunday

Holly

It rained when it should have snowed.
When we went to gather holly

the ditches were swimming, we were wet
to the knees, our hands were all jags

and water ran up our sleeves.
There should have been berries

but the sprigs we brought into the house
gleamed like smashed bottle-glass.

Now here I am, in a room that is decked
with the red-berried, waxy-leafed stuff,

and I almost forget what it's like
to be wet to the skin or longing for snow.

I reach for a book like a doubter
and want it to flare round my hand,

a black-letter bush, a glittering shield-wall
cutting as holly and ice.

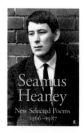

New Selected Poems 1966–1987 (2014)

5 Monday

6 Tuesday

7 Wednesday

8 Thursday

9 Friday

10 Saturday

11 Sunday

Tinderbox

Wild boars blink in the sun. Bolt.
The deer merge with the trees. Birds
fly away between dawn and dusk. Black
spiders dangle and weave. Bunnies
burrow deep. Hornets buzz
between us as we bend
our heads over the map. Blink.
We have lost our bearings
in this atrium of leaf, branch,
twig and trunk.

We cannot find the star-blaze
where the six paths meet. Behold,
I send you forth with your beloved
son. Blinded,
I wait till you disappear over the brink.

The forest catches its breath.
Blanches
when I open the box.
Strike a match. Blow
it out.

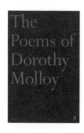

Poems (2019)

12 Monday

13 Tuesday

14 Wednesday

15 Thursday

16 Friday   DAY OF RECONCILIATION (ZA)

17 Saturday   18 Sunday

'We two boys together clinging . . .'

We two boys together clinging,
One the other never leaving,
Up and down the roads going, North and South
    excursions making,
Power enjoying, elbows stretching, fingers clutching,
Arm'd and fearless, eating, drinking, sleeping, loving,
No law less than ourselves owning, sailing, soldiering,
    thieving, threatening,
Misers, menials, priests alarming, air breathing, water
    drinking, on the turf or the sea-beach dancing,
Cities wrenching, ease scorning, statutes mocking,
    feebleness chasing,
Fulfilling our foray.

Winning Words: Inspiring Poems for Everyday Life (2012)

19 Monday

20 Tuesday

21 Wednesday

22 Thursday

23 Friday

24 Saturday CHRISTMAS EVE

25 Sunday CHRISTMAS DAY (UK, IRL)

A Winter Night

It was a chilly winter's night;
　　And frost was glitt'ring on the ground,
And evening stars were twinkling bright;
　　And from the gloomy plain around
　　　　Came no sound,
But where, within the wood-girt tow'r,
The churchbell slowly struck the hour;

As if that all of human birth
　　Had risen to the final day,
And soaring from the wornout earth
　　Were called in hurry and dismay,
　　　　Far away;
And I alone of all mankind
Were left in loneliness behind.

26 **Monday**   BOXING DAY/DAY OF GOODWILL/ST STEPHEN'S DAY
(UK, IRL, AUS, ZA, NZ, CAN)

27 Tuesday   CHRISTMAS DAY OBSERVED (UK, IRL, AUS, ZA, NZ, CAN)

28 Wednesday

29 Thursday

30 Friday

31 **Saturday**   NEW YEAR'S EVE   1   **Sunday**   NEW YEAR'S DAY

A Brief Chronology of Faber's Poetry Publishing

1925 Geoffrey Faber acquires an interest in The Scientific Press and renames the firm Faber and Gwyer. ¶ The poet/bank clerk T. S. Eliot is recruited. 'What will impress my directors favourably is the sense that in you we have found a man who combines literary gifts with business instincts.' – Geoffrey Faber to T. S. Eliot ¶ Eliot brought with him *The Criterion*, the quarterly periodical he had been editing since 1922. (*The Waste Land* had appeared in its first issue, brilliantly establishing its reputation.) He continued to edit it from the Faber offices until it closed in 1939. Though unprofitable, it was hugely influential, introducing early work by Auden, Empson and Spender, among others, and promoting many notable European writers, including Proust and Valéry. ¶ Publication of T. S. Eliot's *Poems, 1909–1925*, which included *The Waste Land* and a new sequence, *The Hollow Men.* ¶

1927 From 1927 to 1931 Faber publishes a series of illustrated pamphlets known as *The Ariel Poems* containing unpublished poems by an eminent poet (Thomas Hardy, W. B. Yeats, Harold Monro, Edith Sitwell and Edmund Blunden, to name but a few) along with an illustration, usually in colour, by a leading contemporary artist (including Eric Gill, Eric Ravilious, Paul Nash and Graham Sutherland). ¶

1928 Faber and Gwyer announce the *Selected Poems of Ezra Pound*, with an introduction and notes by Eliot. ¶

1929 Geoffrey Faber buys out Lady Gwyer and oversees the birth of the Faber and Faber imprint. Legend has it that Walter de la Mare, the father of Faber director Richard de la Mare, suggested the euphonious repetition: another Faber in the company name 'because you can't have too much of a good thing'. ¶

1930 W. H. Auden becomes a Faber poet with a collection entitled simply *Poems.* ¶ Eliot publishes *Ash Wednesday.* ¶

1933 Stephen Spender becomes a Faber poet with his first collection *Poems*, a companion piece to Auden's 1930 work of the same name. ¶ The first British edition of James Joyce's *Pomes Penyeach* is published. ¶

1935 The American poet Marianne Moore publishes with Faber. 'Miss Moore's poems form part of a small body of durable poetry written in our time.' – T. S. Eliot ¶ Louis MacNeice becomes a Faber poet. 'The most original Irish poet of his generation.' – Faber catalogue 1935 ¶

1936 The hugely influential *Faber Book of Modern Verse* (edited by Michael Roberts) is published. ¶

1937 *In Parenthesis* by David Jones is published. 'This is an epic of war. But it is like no other war-book because for the first time that experience has been reduced to "a shape in words." The impression still remains that this book is one of the most remarkable literary achievements of our time.' – *Times Literary Supplement* ¶ W. H. Auden is awarded the Queen's Gold Medal for Poetry. ¶

1939 T. S. Eliot's *Old Possum's Book of Practical Cats* is published with a book jacket illustrated by the author. Originally called *Pollicle Dogs and Jellicle Cats*, the poems were written for his five godchildren. The eldest of these was Geoffrey Faber's son Tom – himself much later a director of Faber and Faber. ¶

1944 Walter de la Mare's *Peacock Pie* is published with illustrations by Edward Ardizzone. ¶

1947 Philip Larkin's first novel, *A Girl in Winter*, is published. 'A young man with an exceptionally clear sense of what, as a writer, he means to do.' – *Times Literary Supplement* ¶

1948 T. S. Eliot wins the Nobel Prize in Literature. ¶

1949 Ezra Pound's *Pisan Cantos* is published. 'The most incomprehensible passages are often more stimulating than much comprehensibility which passes for poetry today.' – *Times Literary Supplement* ¶

1954 *The Ariel Poems* are revived with a new set of pamphlets by W. H. Auden, Stephen Spender, Louis MacNeice, T. S. Eliot, Walter de la Mare, Cecil Day Lewis and Roy Campbell. The artists include Edward Ardizzone, Edward Bawden, Michael Ayrton and John Piper. ¶

1957 Ted Hughes comes to Faber with *The Hawk in the Rain*. ¶ Siegfried Sassoon receives the Queen's Gold Medal for Poetry. ¶

1959 Robert Lowell's collection *Life Studies* is published. ¶

1960 Saint-John Perse wins the Nobel Prize in Literature. ¶

1961 Geoffrey Faber dies. ¶ Ted Hughes's first collection of children's poems, *Meet My Folks*, is published. ¶

1963 The Geoffrey Faber Memorial Prize is established as an annual prize awarded in alternating years to a single volume of poetry or fiction by a Commonwealth author under forty. ¶

1964 Philip Larkin's *The Whitsun Weddings* is published. ¶

1965 T. S. Eliot dies. ¶ Sylvia Plath's posthumous collection, *Ariel*, is published. 'Her extraordinary achievement, poised as she was between volatile emotional state and the edge of the precipice.' – Frieda Hughes ¶ Philip Larkin is awarded the Queen's Gold Medal for Poetry. ¶

1966 Seamus Heaney comes to Faber with *Death of a Naturalist*. ¶ Sylvia Plath's novel *The Bell Jar* is published by Faber. ¶

1968 Ted Hughes's *The Iron Man* is published. ¶

1971 Stephen Spender is awarded the Queen's Gold Medal for Poetry. ¶

1973 Paul Muldoon comes to Faber with his first collection, *New Weather*. ¶

1974 Ted Hughes receives the Queen's Gold Medal for Poetry. ¶

1977 Tom Paulin comes to Faber with his first collection, *A State of Justice*. ¶ Norman Nicholson receives the Queen's Gold Medal for Poetry. ¶

1980 Czesław Miłosz wins the Nobel Prize in Literature. ¶

1981 *Cats*, the Andrew Lloyd Webber musical based on *Old Possum's Book of Practical Cats*, opens in London. ¶

1984 *Rich*, a collection by Faber's own poetry editor, Craig Raine, is published. 'Puts us in touch with life as unexpectedly and joyfully as early Pasternak.' – John Bayley ¶ Ted Hughes becomes Poet Laureate. ¶

1985 Douglas Dunn's collection *Elegies* is the Whitbread Book of the Year. ¶

1986 Vikram Seth's *The Golden Gate* is published. ¶

1987 Seamus Heaney's *The Haw Lantern* wins the Whitbread Poetry Award. ¶

1988 Derek Walcott is awarded the Queen's Gold Medal for Poetry. ¶

1992 Derek Walcott wins the Nobel Prize in Literature. ¶ Thom Gunn's collection *The Man with the Night Sweats* wins the Forward Poetry Prize for Best Collection, while Simon Armitage's *Kid* wins Best First Collection. ¶

1993 Andrew Motion wins the Whitbread Biography Award for his book on Philip Larkin. ¶ Don Paterson's *Nil Nil* wins the Forward Poetry Prize for Best First Collection. ¶

1994 Paul Muldoon wins the T. S. Eliot Prize for *The Annals of Chile*. ¶ Alice Oswald wins an Eric Gregory Award. ¶

1995 Seamus Heaney wins the Nobel Prize in Literature. ¶

1996 Wisława Szymborska wins the Nobel Prize in Literature. ¶ Seamus Heaney's *The Spirit Level* wins the Whitbread Book of the Year Award. 'Touched by a sense of wonder.' – Blake Morrison ¶

1997 Don Paterson wins the T. S. Eliot Prize for *God's Gift to Women*. ¶ Lavinia Greenlaw wins the Forward Prize for Best Single Poem for 'A World Where News Travelled Slowly'. ¶ Ted Hughes's *Tales from Ovid* is the Whitbread Book of the Year. 'A breathtaking book.' – John Carey ¶

1998 Ted Hughes wins the Whitbread Book of the Year for the second time running with *Birthday Letters*, which also wins the T. S. Eliot Prize. 'Language like lava, its molten turmoils hardening into jagged shapes.' – John Carey ¶ Ted Hughes is awarded the Order of Merit. ¶ Christopher Logue receives the Wilfred Owen Poetry Award. ¶

1999 Seamus Heaney's *Beowulf* wins the Whitbread Book of the Year Award. '[Heaney is the] one living poet who can rightly claim to be Beowulf's heir.' – *New York Times* ¶ A memorial service for Ted Hughes is held at Westminster Abbey. In his speech Seamus Heaney calls Hughes 'a guardian spirit of the land and language'. ¶ Hugo Williams wins the T. S. Eliot Prize for his collection *Billy's Rain*. ¶ Andrew Motion is appointed Poet Laureate. ¶

2000 Seamus Heaney receives the Wilfred Owen Poetry Award. ¶

2002 Alice Oswald wins the T. S. Eliot Prize for Poetry for her collection *Dart*. ¶

2003 Paul Muldoon is awarded the Pulitzer Prize for Poetry for *Moy Sand and Gravel*. *Landing Light* by Don Paterson wins the Whitbread Poetry Award. ¶

2004 August Kleinzahler receives the International Griffin Poetry Prize for *The Strange Hours Travellers Keep*. ¶ Hugo Williams is awarded the Queen's Gold Medal for Poetry. ¶

2005 David Harsent wins the Forward Prize for Best Collection for *Legion*. ¶ Harold Pinter receives the Wilfred Owen Poetry Award. ¶ Charles Simic receives the International Griffin Poetry Prize for *Selected Poems 1963–2003*. ¶ Nick Laird wins an Eric Gregory Award. ¶

2006 Christopher Logue wins the Whitbread Poetry Award for *Cold Calls*. ¶ The Geoffrey Faber Memorial Prize is awarded to Alice Oswald for *Woods Etc.* ¶ Seamus Heaney wins the T. S. Eliot Prize for *District and Circle*. ¶

2007 Tony Harrison is awarded the Wilfred Owen Poetry Award. ¶ Daljit Nagra wins the Forward Prize for Best First Collection for *Look We Have Coming to Dover!* ¶ James Fenton receives the Queen's Gold Medal for Poetry. ¶

2008 Daljit Nagra wins the South Bank Show / Arts Council Decibel Award. ¶ Mick Imlah's collection *The Lost Leader* wins the Forward Prize for Best Collection. ¶

2009 Carol Ann Duffy becomes Poet Laureate. ¶ Don Paterson's *Rain* wins the Forward Poetry Prize for Best Collection, while *The Striped World* by Emma Jones wins the Best First Collection Prize. ¶

2010 *The Song of Lunch* by Christopher Reid is shortlisted for the Ted Hughes Award for New Work in Poetry and he is awarded the Costa Poetry Award for *A Scattering*. ¶ The John Florio Prize for Italian Translation 2010 is awarded to Jamie McKendrick for *The Embrace*. ¶ Derek Walcott wins both the Warwick Prize and the T. S. Eliot Prize for Poetry for his collection *White Egrets*. ¶ *Rain* by Don Paterson is shortlisted for the Saltire Scottish Book of the Year. ¶ Tony Harrison is awarded the Prix Européen de Littérature. ¶ The Keats–Shelley Prize is awarded to Simon Armitage for his poem 'The Present'. ¶ The Forward Prize for Best Collection is awarded to Seamus Heaney for *Human Chain*. ¶ Also shortlisted for the Forward Prize for Best Collection are Lachlan Mackinnon for *Small Hours* and Jo Shapcott for *Of Mutability*. ¶ The Centre for Literacy in Primary Education (CLPE) Poetry Prize is awarded to Carol Ann Duffy for *New and Collected Poems for Children*. ¶ Alice Oswald wins the Ted Hughes Award for New Work in Poetry for *Weeds and Wild Flowers*. ¶ *The Striped World* by Emma Jones is shortlisted for the Adelaide Festival Poetry Award. ¶ The Queen's Gold Medal for Poetry is awarded to Don Paterson. ¶

2011 *Of Mutability* by Jo Shapcott is the Costa Book of the Year. ¶ *Human Chain* by Seamus Heaney and *Maggot* by Paul Muldoon are both shortlisted for the *Irish Times* Poetry Now Award. ¶ *Night* by David Harsent is shortlisted for the Forward Prize for Best Collection. ¶ 'Bees' by Jo Shapcott is shortlisted for the Forward Prize for Best Single Poem. ¶ A new digital edition of T. S. Eliot's *The Waste Land* for iPad is launched, bringing to life one of the most revolutionary poems of the last hundred years, illuminated by a wealth of interactive features. ¶ The Queen's Gold Medal for Poetry is awarded to Jo Shapcott. ¶ At Westminster Abbey a memorial is dedicated to Ted Hughes in Poets' Corner. ¶

2012 *The Death of King Arthur* by Simon Armitage is shortlisted for the T. S. Eliot Prize. ¶ *The World's Two Smallest Humans* by Julia Copus is shortlisted for the T. S. Eliot Prize and the Costa Poetry Award. ¶ David Harsent's collection *Night* wins the International Griffin Poetry Prize. ¶ *81 Austerities* by Sam Riviere wins the Felix Dennis Prize for Best First Collection, one of the Forward Prizes for Poetry. ¶ *Farmers Cross* by Bernard O'Donoghue is shortlisted for the *Irish Times* Poetry Now Award. ¶

2013 The Forward Prize for Best First Collection is awarded to Emily Berry for *Dear Boy*. ¶ Hugo Williams is shortlisted for the Forward Prize for Best Single

Poem for 'From the Dialysis Ward'. ¶ Alice Oswald is awarded the Warwick Prize for Writing for her collection *Memorial*, which also wins the Poetry Society's Corneliu M. Popescu Prize for poetry in translation. ¶ The Queen's Gold Medal for Poetry is awarded to Douglas Dunn. ¶ The shortlist for the T. S. Eliot Prize includes Daljit Nagra for *The Ramayana: A Retelling* and Maurice Riordan for *The Water Stealer*. ¶ *Pink Mist* by Owen Sheers wins the Hay Festival Medal for Poetry. ¶ In his eulogy for Seamus Heaney, Paul Muldoon says, 'We remember the beauty of Seamus Heaney – as a bard, and in his being.' In November the first official tribute evenings to Heaney are held at Harvard, then in New York, followed by events at the Royal Festival Hall in London, the Waterfront Hall, Belfast, and the Sheldonian, Oxford. ¶

2014 Maurice Riordan is shortlisted for the Pigott Poetry Prize for *The Water Stealer*. ¶ Hugo Williams is shortlisted for the Forward Prize for Best Collection for *I Knew the Bride*. ¶ Daljit Nagra is awarded the Society of Authors Travelling Scholarship. ¶ Nick Laird's *Go Giants* is shortlisted for the *Irish Times* Poetry Now Award. ¶ Emily Berry, Emma Jones and Daljit Nagra are announced as three of the Poetry Book Society's Next Generation Poets 2014. ¶ *Pink Mist* by Owen Sheers is named the Wales Book of the Year after winning the poetry category. ¶

2015 *Fire Songs* by David Harsent is awarded the T. S. Eliot Prize for Poetry. ¶ Alice Oswald wins the Ted Hughes Award for New Work for *Tithonus*, a poem and performance commissioned by London's Southbank Centre. ¶ *One Thousand Things Worth Knowing* by Paul Muldoon wins the Pigott Poetry Prize. ¶ Don Paterson is awarded the Neustadt International Prize for Literature. ¶ *Terror* by Toby Martinez de las Rivas is shortlisted for the Seamus Heaney Centre for Poetry's Prize for First Full Collection. ¶ Paul Muldoon's *One Thousand Things Worth Knowing* is shortlisted for the Forward Prize for Best Collection. ¶ James Fenton is awarded the Pen Pinter Prize. ¶ *40 Sonnets* by Don Paterson wins the Costa Poetry Award, and is shortlisted for the T. S. Eliot Prize. ¶

2016 Don Paterson is shortlisted for the International Griffin Poetry Prize. ¶ *40 Sonnets* by Don Paterson is shortlisted for the Saltire Society Literary Awards. ¶ *The Seasons of Cullen Church* by Bernard O'Donoghue is shortlisted for the T. S. Eliot Prize. ¶ Jack Underwood receives a Somerset Maugham Award. ¶ An excerpt from *Salt* by David Harsent is shortlisted for the Forward Prize for Best Single Poem. ¶

2017 *The Unaccompanied* by Simon Armitage, *Stranger, Baby* by Emily Berry and *The Noise of a Fly* by Douglas Dunn all receive Recommendations from the Poetry Book Society. They also give a Special Commendation to *Selected Poems of Thom*

Gunn, edited by Clive Wilmer. ¶ Simon Armitage receives the PEN Award for Poetry in Translation for *Pearl* ¶ Bernard O'Donoghue's collection *The Seasons of Cullen Church* is shortlisted for the Pigott Poetry Prize. ¶ Emily Berry's collection *Stranger, Baby* is shortlisted for the Forward Prize for Best Collection. ¶ Sam Riviere's collection *Kim Kardashian's Marriage* is shortlisted for the Ledbury Poetry Prize. ¶ Douglas Dunn's collection *The Noise of a Fly* is shortlisted for the T. S. Eliot Prize. ¶ Paul Muldoon is awarded the Queen's Gold Medal for Poetry. ¶

2018 Matthew Francis's collection *The Mabinogi* is shortlisted for the Ted Hughes Award and Welsh Book of the Year. ¶ Toby Martinez de las Rivas's collection *Black Sun* is shortlisted for the Forward Prize for Best Collection. ¶ Richard Scott's collection *Soho* is shortlisted for the Forward Prize for Best First Collection, the T. S. Eliot Prize and the Costa Poetry Award. ¶ Owen Sheers is the recipient of the Wilfred Owen Poetry Award for 2018. ¶ Daljit Nagra receives a Society of Authors Cholmondeley Award. ¶ Seamus Heaney's collection *100 Poems* is shortlisted for the 2018 Books Are My Bag Readers Awards, Poetry category. ¶ Nick Laird's collection *Feel Free* is shortlisted for the T. S. Eliot Prize. ¶ Zaffar Kunial's collection *Us* is shortlisted for the Costa Poetry Award and the T. S. Eliot Prize. ¶ Hannah Sullivan's collection

Three Poems is shortlisted for the Roehampton Poetry Prize and the Costa Poetry Award, and goes on to win the T. S. Eliot Prize. ¶ Simon Armitage is awarded the Queen's Gold Medal for Poetry. ¶

2019 Simon Armitage is appointed Poet Laureate. ¶ Richard Scott's collection *Soho* is shortlisted for the Roehampton Poetry Prize and the Polari First Book Prize. ¶ Hannah Sullivan's collection *Three Poems* wins the John Pollard Foundation International Poetry Prize and is shortlisted for the Ted Hughes Award, the Seamus Heaney First Collection Prize and the Michael Murphy Memorial Prize. ¶ Sophie Collins's collection *Who Is Mary Sue?* is shortlisted for the 2018 Saltire Society's Scottish Poetry Book of the Year and wins both the Michael Murphy Memorial Prize and an Eric Gregory Award. ¶ Ishion Hutchinson's collection *House of Lords and Commons* wins the Windham-Campbell Prize. ¶ Lavinia Greenlaw's collection *The Built Moment* is shortlisted for the Roehampton Poetry Prize and the East Anglian Book Award (poetry category). ¶ Zaffar Kunial's collection *Us* is shortlisted for the 2019 Rathbones Folio Prize, the Roehampton Poetry Prize and the Michael Murphy Memorial Prize. ¶ 'The Window' from Mary Jean Chan's collection *Flèche* is shortlisted for the Forward Prize for Best Single Poem and her poem 'The Fencer' wins the Geoffrey Dearmer Prize. ¶ Poems from Rachael Allen,

Lavinia Greenlaw, Paul Muldoon and Hugo Williams are Highly Commended for the Forward Prizes for Poetry. ¶ Ilya Kaminsky's collection *Deaf Republic* is shortlisted for the Forward Prize for Best Collection, the T. S. Eliot Prize and the US National Book Award (poetry category). ¶

2020 Mary Jean Chan's collection *Flèche* wins the Costa Poetry Award and is shortlisted for both the John Pollard International Poetry Prize and the Seamus Heaney First Collection Poetry Prize. ¶ Nick Laird's collection *Feel Free* is shortlisted for the Derek Walcott Poetry Prize. ¶ Julia Copus's collection *Girlhood* is shortlisted for the Derek Walcott Poetry Prize. ¶ Paul Muldoon's collection *Frolic and Detour* is shortlisted for the *Irish Times* Poetry Now Award. ¶ Natalie Diaz's collection *Postcolonial Love Poem* is shortlisted for the T. S. Eliot Prize and the US National Book Award (poetry category). ¶

Acknowledgements

Poetry

All poetry reprinted by permission of Faber & Faber unless otherwise stated.

'Rainglobe' taken from *Us* © Zaffar Kunial ¶ 'Winter Trees' taken from *Collected Poems* © The Estate of Sylvia Plath ¶ 'Canopy' taken from *Stranger, Baby* © Emily Berry ¶ 'Alpha Step' taken from *A Year in the New Life* © Jack Underwood ¶ 'Every' taken from *Anecdotal Evidence* © Wendy Cope ¶ 'Spiegel im Spiegel' taken from *Living Weapon* © Rowan Ricardo Phillips, reprinted by permission of Faber & Faber and Farrar Straus & Giroux, LLC, New York ¶ 'Last' taken from *Sandettie Light Vessel Automatic* © Simon Armitage ¶ 'The Iron Age Boat at Caumatruish' taken from *Selected Poems* © Bernard O'Donoghue ¶ 'Solar' taken from *The Complete Poems* © The Estate of Philip Larkin ¶ 'A Glass of Wine' taken from *Public Property* © Andrew Motion ¶ '31' taken from *After Fame* © Sam Riviere ¶ 'WCW' taken from *Doves* © Lachlan Mackinnon ¶ 'Creature' taken from *Wing* © Matthew Francis ¶ 'Star' taken from *The Poetry of Derek Walcott 1948–2013* © The Estate of Derek Walcott ¶ 'Preludes I' taken from *The Poems of T. S. Eliot: Volume I* © Set Copyrights ¶ 'Remembrance Day' (from 'Out') taken from *Collected Poems* © The Estate of Ted Hughes ¶ 'I May, I Might, I Must' taken from *New Collected Poems* © The Estate of Marianne Moore reprinted by permission of Faber & Faber and Farrar Straus & Giroux ¶ 'Inkling' taken from *The World's Two Smallest Humans* © Julia Copus ¶ 'Holly' taken from *New Selected Poems 1966–1987* © The Estate of Seamus Heaney ¶ 'Tinderbox' taken from *Poems* © The Estate of Dorothy Molloy

The Faber Book of 20th Century Women's Poetry, edited by Fleur Adock, design by Pentagram
British Museum by Daljit Nagra, design by Faber, series design by Pentagram
The Poetical Works of Rupert Brooke edited by Geoffrey Keynes, design by Berthold Wolpe
Collected Poems 1925–1948 by Louis MacNeice, design by Berthold Wolpe
One Lark, One Horse by Michael Hofmann, design by Faber, series design by Pentagram
The Faber Book of Modern European Poetry edited by A. Alvarez, design by Pentagram
Elizabethan and Jacobean Poets edited by John Danby, design by Berthold Wolpe
William Blake edited by James Fenton, design by Faber, illustration by Mark Cazalet
The Faber Book of Twentieth Century Verse, edited by John Heath-Stubbs and David Wright, design by Berthold Wolpe
Old Possum's Book of Practical Cats read by Lemn Sissay, design by Faber
Photograph © Jeff Cottenden, illustrations by Júlia Sardà
The Funny Side: 101 Humorous Poems edited by Wendy Cope, design by Faber
Deaf Republic by Ilya Kaminsky, design by Faber, series design by Pentagram
Dolphins by Stephen Spender, design by Pentagram

Every effort has been made to trace or contact all copyright holders. The publishers would be pleased to rectify at the earliest opportunity any omissions or errors brought to their notice.

NOTES

NOTES